£4.95

Mind your language!

'Literacy for Active Citizenship' series

Written by Enuma Madu
Illustrated by Hugo Dudley

Mind your language!
© Learning Unlimited 2015

Published by Learning Unlimited Ltd as part of the Active Citizenship and English (ACE) project. The ACE project, led by Learning Unlimited, was funded through the European Integration Fund and delivered in partnership with Blackfriars Settlement, Working Men's College and the UCL Institute of Education.

Foreword

The ACE project
'Literacy for Active Citizenship' series

The Active Citizenship and English (ACE) project, led by Learning Unlimited and delivered in partnership with Blackfriars Settlement, Working Men's College and the UCL Institute of Education, received funding from the European Integration Fund (July 2013 to June 2015).

The ACE project aimed to support non-EU women to develop their skills and confidence in English and to take an active part in everyday life in the UK. As part of the project we wanted to produce a series of readers for our learners, and other adults also settling in the UK, which include stories about funny, personal and less typical aspects of everyday life in the UK. These stories were written by learners and volunteer befrienders on the ACE project and edited by ESOL specialists at Learning Unlimited. The supporting activities were also developed by the Learning Unlimited team.

We hope you enjoy using the 'Literacy for Active Citizenship' series.

To find out more about the ACE project, please see:
www.learningunlimited.co/projects/ace

Ngozi and Ifeoma come from Nigeria.
They both speak Igbo and they both love
shopping. One day they went shopping
for clothes in London.

Ngozi and Ifeoma went into a large
clothes shop on Oxford Street and
they spent hours choosing and trying
on clothes. At last, they decided what
they wanted and took the clothes to
the checkout.

The checkout was very busy so they waited in a long queue. As they were waiting, Ngozi noticed one of the checkout assistants.

He was a tall, young, white man with spiky red, green and blue hair. He also had a lot of earrings in his ears, nose and lips.

Ngozi laughed. In Igbo, she said to Ifeoma in a loud voice, "Look at that young man, the one with the coloured hair."

Ifeoma answered in Igbo, "He looks like a chicken in the rain." Ngozi then said, "He thinks he's handsome but he looks really silly!"

When Ngozi and Ifeoma got to the
checkout, the man with the coloured hair
served them. Ngozi continued talking
about him in Igbo as he scanned their
clothes.

The young man was very polite and smiled at them. He folded their clothes neatly into bags and they paid. As they left the checkout he called out to them in Igbo, "Have a nice day!"

Ngozi and Ifeoma were surprised and very embarrassed!

Key words

checkout	the place where you pay in a shop
embarrassed	feel bad about something you did or said
handsome	attractive / good-looking
Igbo	a Nigerian language
queue	a line of people waiting to pay
silly	funny and strange
serve	to help or take money from customers
spiky	pointed

Questions

1. Why did Ngozi and Ifeoma go to Oxford Street?

2. What did Ngozi and Ifeoma do when they were in the queue?

3. How do you think the young man felt when he heard Ngozi and Ifeoma talking about him?

4. Why did Ngozi and Ifeoma feel embarrassed when they left the shop?

5. Have you ever been surprised when someone understood or spoke your language?

6. Describe a time when you felt embarrassed.

7. Do you enjoy shopping for clothes? Describe something you bought recently.

Activities

Role play

Work in pairs. One learner is the young man with the coloured hair. The other learner is his friend.

Role play a telephone conversation between the two friends. Use some of these phrases:

- How are you?

- Guess what happened today at work.

- What happened?

- Oh no!

- And then what?

- How do you feel now?

- Don't laugh. It isn't funny.

For more downloadable activities, visit:
www.learningunlimited.co/resources/publications

Acknowledgements

Mind your language! was written by Enuma Madu and illustrated by Hugo Dudley. We are grateful to them for being able to include their work as part of the 'Literacy for Active Citizenship' series.